CAN YOU HEAR ME?

MARGARET JUMMY TARIBO

ILLUSTRATED BY
TOLU SHOFULE

DISTINCT™
FAMILY SERVICES LTD

CAN YOU HEAR ME?

Margaret Jummy Taribo
Illustrated by Tolu Shofule

Published by
Distinct Famiy Services Ltd.
76 Millard Road
London SE8 3GB
United Kingdom

Email: info@distinctfamilyservices.com
Website: www.distinctfamilyservices.com

First published 2024

ISBN: 978-1-9196147-1-7

Cover design / book layout: Imaginovation Ltd.
Cover illustration by Tolu Shofule

Printed in the United Kingdom.

CONTENTS

FOREWARD

As a lawyer with expertise in criminal law, a community activist, and more recently, the Mayor of the London Borough of Southwark, I have, over the last 15 years, had the chance to witness how the support offered by society affects the life prospects of our most vulnerable individuals. I've observed firsthand how policy choices can expand and restrict life opportunities for young people and children. Moreover, I've witnessed the repercussions society faces when a young person's or child's life veers out of control, leaving it to deal with the aftermath.

What resonates with me is the importance of prioritising these individuals' needs in all we do. When we get it right with their well-being from the outset, they are more likely to mature into productive contributors to society. Fundamentally, this entails ensuring that they have a voice in determining the services established to aid them. That's why I've consistently advocated for Southwark's youth services to incorporate a significant element of youth input.

I've had the privilege of collaborating with various individuals, including disaffected youths. Among them, first-time offenders hold a special place in my heart. This sentiment has led me to advocate for a targeted approach to address antisocial behaviours, with a particular emphasis on expanding youth-funded activities to curb reoffending rates. In the course of this work, I've reflected on the underlying reasons why young people end up in challenging circumstances. While individuals must always be accountable for their criminal actions, my interactions with diverse community members have raised questions about whether these children, especially those from marginalised ethnic communities, are truly being heard and empowered. I firmly believe that, as a society, we can do much more.

Research has shown a correlation between insufficient funding for youth and family support services and disparities in health, education, and employment opportunities within our communities. Numerous families are grappling with these challenges and would benefit from early intervention to address critical issues. Nevertheless, many families are left to navigate a system they may not fully comprehend. Moreover, their upbringing in diverse cultural environments significantly influences their children's social and emotional well-being. Hence, it's crucial to intervene as early as possible.

The story in this book, Can You Hear Me? subtly highlights these issues. Every individual in our society – parents, educators and systems

– plays a vital role in ensuring our children are heard and truly listened to. This is the only way to reduce inequalities and improve their mental well-being. Additionally, it is crucial to support parents who may not have a voice so they can develop the confidence to prioritise their children's development over cultural or traditional barriers. The book also helps shed light on various issues that can benefit professionals, parents, and children without being judgmental. Although it may not provide all the answers we seek, it does raise awareness about the challenges faced by black and underrepresented families and the importance of promoting cultural competencies.

Councillor Michael Situ

Mayor of Southwark (2023/2024)

ACKNOWLEDGEMENTS

I want to thank my husband, David Taribo, for his unwavering support, especially as I embarked on the journey of writing this book. I deeply cherish your loving encouragement. My children, 'Priye and Abigail, have been an invaluable source of insight and motivation, particularly as young people. You are truly remarkable.

I appreciate my team at ParentSkills2Go, who have been hugely instrumental in providing the support and enabling environment to get this work done. A heartfelt 'thank you' goes out to our dedicated parent volunteers and young volunteers, who play a massive role in the work we do in the community. I've had the privilege of learning so much working with you, which has greatly influenced this story's writing. This acknowledgement extends to Stephanie, Stella, Hannah, Olivia, Prisca, Georgina, Prisca,

Jeannette, and their parents, who continuously nurture their children's creative expressions.

I'm thankful for the ongoing support of my spiritual mentor, Rev. (Dr) Anthony Jegede, who is my reliable source of encouragement. Tolu Shofule, the dedication, passion, and meticulous attention to detail you put into this work are deeply appreciated. Michael Adeleye, thank you for your dogged belief in me and for going the extra mile to see us succeed with excellence. Bambo, thank you for infusing this project with invaluable creativity and passion.

Many thanks to the young people who have inspired the writing of this book. I also appreciate colleagues in the community who work with kindness and tirelessly to support families in the community.

To my dear sister, Bolaji Sanyaolu, thank you as always for your excellence, dedication, and commitment to ensuring this book gets published. Many thanks also to my other siblings, Dipo, Yemisi, and Folusho, who look up to me and have seen me grow over the years.

Most of all, my Maker, the Lord God Almighty, who brought me from nothing, built me up and gave me a platform to fulfil my dream. Thank You, Lord!

DEDICATION

This book is dedicated to every child and young individual navigating cultural conflicts and barriers. They deserve appreciation, attention, and recognition as the generation capable of effecting positive change.

PREFACE

When I initially conceived the title of this book – *"Can You Hear Me?"* – what came to mind was the hectic rush of my children's school runs from years past. I vividly recall the constant hustle, feeling perpetually pressed for time. To be frank, I felt as though I had little choice in the matter. I needed to work long hours to cover the bills and have a little extra for my personal 'wants'. At the same time, I yearned to be there for my children during drop-offs and pickups, to be fully present and ensure they were doing well. Yet, it seemed even that was beyond my grasp. I distinctly remember a moment when my daughter attempted to communicate a school-related issue, and it became apparent that I wasn't genuinely attentive. When she finally managed to capture my attention, she expressed in her three-year-old manner that

'I wasn't hearing' and that I was also failing to listen. This book, rooted in real-life encounters, takes us into these two aspects of hearing and really listening, not just for children but also for parents, caregivers, and professionals engaged with families.

The phrase *"Can You Hear Me?"* within the context of this book can serve as both a question and a statement. It represents the sentiments, observations, curiosity and realisations that children and young adults harbour regarding the adults and authority figures in their lives, particularly their parents and teachers. Through my interactions with young people as a community practitioner, I've encountered this question often, prompting me to ponder: Do we, as adults, truly listen to our children's unspoken pleas for assistance? Can we empathise with their anguish, frustration, uncertainty, and fear? Have we contemplated the possibility that our hearing may sometimes be selective, influenced by our circumstances and experiences? I, too, am guilty of approaching my children with the assumption that I am always right as the adult in the situation. Believe me, this is a widespread issue in many cultures, shaped by upbringing, tradition, and societal norms.

The book recounts the story of Abena, a young woman whose silent cry for help from a young age goes unheard by her mother and other authority figures in her life. It depicts how this profoundly influenced her upbringing and transition into adulthood. The narrative reflects the unspoken experiences of numerous young individuals from African, Caribbean, Asian, and other ethnic minority backgrounds who are raised in a foreign country. It delves into how these individuals grapple with conflicts within their homes and families stemming from their parents' beliefs and cultural clashes, sometimes affecting their mental well-being. These same children must navigate the educational system in the United Kingdom, where there may not be sufficient cultural understanding to provide adequate support. The challenges encountered within this context can escalate to more severe issues, such as school exclusion and involvement in criminal activities. The book underscores the struggles related to mental health due to the lack of familial support and the desire to find a fulfilling career path that offers a sense of purpose.

"Can You Hear Me?" isn't just a story; it also amplifies the voices of young individuals who articulate their own and others' realities through authentic, creative, and deeply felt poetry.

As both a parent and a professional, I consider it an honour to collaborate with families in my work. It has been a humbling journey for me as I've strived to appreciate and value the experiences of young people while also letting go of my own preconceptions as an individual of African heritage. I aim to bridge the gap between young people and their families by actively listening to and acknowledging their perspectives. While this book may not offer all the solutions, it intends to raise awareness among young people, parents, caregivers, and professionals regarding these issues and to foster the creation of a society where young people can flourish because their voices are genuinely heard. I hope you find it enriching.

PROLOGUE

Present Day

"Muummm!" Abena dropped the knife suddenly as she heard her daughter's scream and turned round to see her burst through the kitchen door. "Mum!" Queen breathed deeply. "I told you – no, I begged you – not to buy slip-on sneakers. High-top, I said. High-top". Abena silently let out a sigh of relief. Her fourteen-year-old was not hurt. "Queen..." she started, getting ready to smack her daughter down for her tone. But Queen continued: "I'm going to be a laughingstock in school. I will not be able to raise my head ever again!" she glared at no one in particular. Abena counted to ten as her daughter continued to have a meltdown. "Queen", her mum repeated. "Stop being so dramatic". She took the sneakers from her daughter and inspected her purchase with an element of pride. "What are you talking about?! I know this is what you young people wear these days. Besides, they're expensive. You should be grateful". Queen looked at her mother as if she had just crawled out from under a rock and said, "Mum. First of all, no one is wearing these in my school anymore, and second of all, it's not about the price, it's about the trendiness. These ones are not trending!' She moaned as if in pain. Abena felt like giving her the back of her hand, but she reminded herself that they no longer did that. She sighed in frustration and went back to cutting the vegetables, leaving Queen to heave and sigh continuously for the next five minutes. She sent a prayer to heaven before turning back to her daughter. She couldn't help but be amused by the sight of Queen slumped at the kitchen table, staring at the shoes intently as if to make them disappear by some form of magic.

"Queen, what did I tell you about gratitude?" Her daughter looked up, and Abena could see that she was close to tears. With all that was happening in the environment, she really couldn't understand why this was like the end of the world for Queen. Her daughter brought herself to respond to her mum's question, "You said we should be thankful for what we have and that when we receive a gift, we should say thank you first, even if we do not like it", she mumbled. "So ...?" her mum asked, expectantly. "Thank you for the shoes, Mum. I'm sorry for reacting as I did. I was just shocked when I saw them".

'Shocked' seemed extreme to Abena, but then, what did she know? Queen continued, "It's hard sometimes, Mum, especially if you don't fit in with your mates". Abena softened. "I hear you, darling, but be more respectful when expressing your thoughts. And remember, you can't always have everything you want".

With that 'teachable moment' out of the way, Abena said, "You know what? We'll take them back tomorrow and get the' trending' ones. How about that? " Queen sprung up from the kitchen chair and hugged her mum. "Thanks, Mum. You're the best!". "Oh, so I am the best now, am I?" Abena asked teasingly. She caught sight of her husband peeping, conveniently after the crisis had been averted. Abena rolled her eyes at him as he said in his defence: "You know our football team is playing, Hon. I just need to get some drinks. You've got this" he smiled mischievously, grabbed the drinks, and quickly made his escape. Abena shook her head affectionately. She was glad that at least her nine-year-old son, Femi Junior, was occupied with the match with his father—one 'crisis' at a time.

Now that Queen was in a better frame of mind, Abena asked her about her day in school. As her daughter helped around in the kitchen, it was like a floodgate opening. She spoke animatedly about everything that happened that day in school – her new English teacher (not liked by anyone), the bully (he should not try his nonsense with her), a new girl (she was both beautiful and bright) and so on. Her face, however, took on a pensive look when the conversation moved to her best friend, Esi. "Mum, you know that Esi's issue at home has not been resolved. Her mum is so nasty to her!" Abena chose not to interrupt her daughter. "Can you imagine? She was grounded for two weeks just because she got a 'C' in Economics! "C" is still a good grade! And she even got 'As' and 'Bs' in all the other subjects. But that's not all; she can't talk to her mum or dad about anything. It's as if they hate her. "Queen". Abena interjected, "Hate is a strong word. They must mean well". Queen pursed her lips. "Mum, seriously. Think about it," she gestured towards her mother, "You are very busy, and you take time to listen to me. You ask about everything that is going on with me. I just feel so bad for Esi. Do you know that when she just started her period, I was the one she opened up to about it? She didn't even know what to do!" Abena looked at her daughter and thought about what she was saying. It all sounded so familiar... in another life.

Chapter One

NO LOVE?

"Abena, are you going to spend all day at that window?" ten-year-old Abena heard her mother say sharply. "Go outside and join your friends, or whatever". Adwoa wasn't too worried that Abena was indoors instead of playing outside with her friends during the summer break, but she was irritated that she had not moved from the window for over two hours. Due to the sunny weather, the Estate was filled with children playing games and enjoying the warm climate. These were children whose parents couldn't

afford lavish vacations, and Abena fell into this category.

As the sun began to set and the clock struck 5.00 pm, Abena was still standing by the window, peering through the blinds and looking out into

their small neighbourhood. She then felt the impact of her mother's anxiety and frustration as she raised her voice, "Abena, leave that spot and come tidy up this room right away!" Abena couldn't understand why her mother would want to raise her voice, except for the obvious reason that her father, Adwoa's husband, Kofi had been gone all day. She later found out that, as much as she adored her father, his presence at home only added to Adwoa's stress and frustration as an unfulfilled stay-at-home housewife and mother. Even if her mother loved her, Abena sensed that it was rarely demonstrated towards her. "Abena!" she yelled louder this time, and a startled Abena reacted with fear at the sound of her mother's voice. "I'm sorry, Mummy," she said turning away from the window and picking up the scattered clothing items on the living room sofa. Her actions were half-hearted, as her thoughts were filled with questions about where her father could be. Why wasn't he home yet? Was she the reason why he was not here? She tried her best not to think so, but she remembered waking up to the voices of her parents having a big fight that morning.

She had heard raised voices, angry words, and crying. It wasn't the first time she had heard or witnessed her parents argue, and usually, they would get so wrapped up in their argument that they would ignore her presence, her tears and her pleas for them to stop. She had learned to cope by tuning out the noise with music or isolating herself in the bathroom. However, this fight was different because what she overheard reinforced her belief that she was not cherished, increasing her feelings of insecurity and inadequacy.

Adwoa had woken up that day to Kofi getting ready to leave home earlier than usual. "Where are you off to, if I may ask?" She said. Kofi responded rudely, "No, you may not ask. And don't even start with me this morning". She got off the bed and yelled angrily at him, "You have started again!" Before he could respond, she went off on a tirade, "You act as if I am a burden to you. Nobody forced you to marry

me o. And don't even bring up my getting
pregnant! You could have said no even then! I
would have managed without you. My parents
would have gotten used to the fact that I was a
single mother!" Kofi looked at her with disdain

and said, "Really? So now you want to play 'my parents' card? Were your parents responsible for your carelessness? Answer me! Were they the ones who trapped me into marrying you?" Adwoa responded, "So you still think I did it to trap you? Hmmm." Kofi cut her off, "I don't care anymore! The only positive thing that has come out of this whole mess is lovely Abena, but even her goodness doesn't erase the frustration I have experienced over the years!" He made to leave but she blocked his exit. "What are you still doing here then?" "You are absolutely useless as a husband and a father". She smacked her lips in disgust, and that seemed to be the end of it. But then she continued by asking, "Do you honestly believe that the short amount of time you spend with your daughter can compensate for your lack of care for this family? You must be more self-centred than I thought!" Kofi fired back, "Can you blame me? Look at you, a cold-hearted woman incapable of showing her emotions. I would rather be out enjoying my life than be with you." And with that, he shoved her out of the way and walked out.

Even though Abena did not fully grasp the argument, she remembered that her dad had mentioned her name, but she was confused as to whether she was 'a positive thing' or 'the cause of frustration'. She did not know how to process this revelation. However, as the argument continued, it became clear to Abena that she had been an unplanned pregnancy and that her father was forced into marrying her mother when he was only 19.

Adwoa had come from a strict upbringing in Ghana, West Africa, and had limited exposure to relationships with the opposite sex. She met Kofi at a mutual friend's birthday celebration and was captivated by his appearance and the way he treated her. Being inexperienced and naïve,

Adwoa didn't take time to think about whether he was truly suitable for her. Before long, they began having unprotected sex, and this resulted in Adwoa becoming pregnant. When her parents learned of the pregnancy, they insisted that Kofi "do the right thing" and marry their daughter. And he obliged. He was already in the process of planning to relocate to the United Kingdom, so he had to fit Adwoa into his plans by obtaining a visa and travelling with her. Adwoa was so caught up in the excitement and anticipation of going abroad that she didn't have the chance to explore her emotions towards Kofi or her feelings about being pregnant.

They arrived at their new home in Bermondsey during the Spring season, and she was captivated by the beautiful and peaceful surroundings. To sum up, she was thrilled to be here. This was the life she had always longed for. However, the harsh realities slowly began to emerge – first

with the weather. The cold and dampness of Winter was a complete shock to her system. As time went on, she started feeling homesick and isolated without her community of relatives and friends. On the other hand, Kofi was absorbed in his own world, with his only goal being to achieve success. He couldn't comprehend why she had any complaints and started picking fights for no reason–criticising her appearance, the food, and the way the house looked. Before long, they grew apart and had no affection for each other. It was so bad that Adwoa prayed for a miscarriage so that she could return to Ghana. But that didn't happen. Abena was born, and Kofi adored her wholeheartedly. Adwoa, on the other hand, struggled to develop a bond with her child. As it turned out, Kofi's love for the baby was not enough to keep him present or responsible. He preferred to spend time with friends and his imaginary occupations. In the following years, her parents managed to stay together because of Abena, but Adwoa became increasingly frustrated with the fact that Kofi couldn't hold a steady job. Her forced role as a stay-at-home mother added to the tension, which was transferred to Abena, who bore the brunt of Adwoa's anger. This affected Abena's confidence and self-worth.

Despite her parent's tumultuous relationship, Abena had longed for their affection, but this was scarce. Eventually, she tried not to expect much from her mother and looked up to her as simply a parent. However, she lived for her father's love, and his even limited demonstration of this love profoundly impacted her life. She did everything in her power to please him and always wanted to bring a smile to his face and to convince him to stay with her. Thinking back, that was a heavy burden for a child.

It was already 9.00 pm and dark outside, yet no

sign of her father. Abena turned to her mother, hoping to find some answers, but even before she asked, Adwoa simply shrugged and told Abena to go to bed. Abena lay down, tears falling down her cheeks, longing for her mother's comforting embrace. She yearned to hear words of comfort, assuring her that everything would be alright even if her father hadn't come returned. But there was none – no reassurance, no warmth, and no concern. For Abena, it seemed there was no love.

Ahhh!!!

Scream, Shout
My voice hurts.
You waste your voice on meaningless words
When you could be putting it to good use
Words hurt, especially loud ones
Close your lips, it's too loud!

(Precious Airemuen, 10 years)

Chapter Two

AT HOME IN AFRICA

Nothing, they say, lasts forever. At some point, her mother finally took steps to take her life back. She cited one of the many inspiring quotes that had resonated with her in the past, '*You can't just sit there and wait for people to give you that golden dream*'. She wanted her golden dream, and she was going to get it. She decided to leave Kofi and register for a nursing programme. She told Abena it would be tough, so she was going to send her to live with her grandparents in Ghana. Of course, this did not go down well with Abena.

Granted, the abuse and fighting had escalated, but she had hoped it could be managed and everything would eventually be sorted. Never in her wildest imagination did a trip to Africa seem part of the solution. The thought was so far-fetched to her. 'Why?' she asked her Mum in shock. 'Please, Mum, don't send me away. I'll be good, and I'll do better". Abena's pleas only fell on deaf ears. Her Mum just shrugged her shoulders and said she was only doing what was best for Abena.

Abena boarded the flight in a daze. She was headed to a place where she would be staying with people she was unfamiliar with and who probably wouldn't like her. She had hardly ever spoken to her grandparents before, so she had no idea what they were like or what they expected of her. In her mind, she had concluded that nobody seemed pleased with her, so she wondered what she could ever do to make her grandparents happy. Abena was overwhelmed, anxious, and powerless. She dozed off with these troubled emotions and woke up only when the flight attendant came to check if she was properly secured in her seat. The plane would be landing in 30 minutes.

She stepped off the aircraft with a mixture of anxiety and anticipation but was distracted by the enveloping blanket of the hot climate. As she was guided towards a holding area, she barely had a chance to take in her surroundings when she heard her name being announced over the loudspeaker. She then spotted a dignified elderly couple waiting at the entrance. "This must be them," Abena thought, cautiously approaching them. As soon as she saw her grandmother's welcoming smile, all her apprehension melted away. "Akwaaba", Abena's grandmother greeted her in Twi with a warm, welcoming smile. Her grandfather was not very talkative, but this didn't bother Abena. The warmth she felt from her grandmother was already an encouragement for what lay ahead. She decided to embrace this newfound sense of adventure and eagerly anticipated spending time with Nana, as her grandmother was affectionately called.

The feeling of euphoria didn't last long. Nanabarima, as her grandfather was known by everyone in the household, was not easy to please and made sure Abena knew it. "Why didn't you do the dishes before going outside to play? And what did I say about showing me your homework after your chores?!" Clearly, these were not questions that required a response, because he finished off by saying, "I will not allow you to be spoiled in this house. Never!"

Abena didn't know it then but when Adwoa had written home requesting for her parents to take Abena in to spend some time with them,

her father, a disciplinarian to the core, was not happy. He went on his usual anger rant, "Look at where your frivolousness has led you, leaving us to clean up your mess. I don't have a choice but to support you, but I won't tolerate any bad behaviour, especially from a child you would have spoilt." And he wasted no time expressing the same sentiment to Abena, ensuring she followed instructions to the letter. Whenever she fell short, she was promptly disciplined. Thankfully, the ever-loving Nana was always there to comfort her, creating a good balance for her life in Ghana. She came to realise that even her Nanabarima's discipline was just tough love–strict yet caring. It took some getting used to, but she started to appreciate the structure in the household as it helped her learn and succeed in school. She did everything she could to make them proud of her.

Life in the United Kingdom was gradually

fading into the background as Abena settled down and got used to school in Kumasi. It was a reputable school, and even though the teachers were strict, she eventually got to love it. Initially, she found it difficult to make friends because of her British accent and shyness. Her lack of confidence became apparent when, one day, she wore a traditional African dress adorned with the image of a famous artist. Some of her classmates teased her endlessly, calling the artist her 'boyfriend', and this caused Abena to break down in tears and refuse to attend school the following day. Only through her grandparents' persistence and support did she eventually return to school and learn to cope with her classmates' teasing.

Abena also did not enjoy the meals her grandmother prepared at first, especially because of the pepper and spices. But she developed a liking for *Kenke* and fish over time.

The most enjoyable meal for her was breakfast, which consisted of rice, water, sugar, and milk, taken along with fresh bread. Having evaporated tinned milk (common in that part of the world) in tea was a delightful experience, and she took pleasure in punching a hole in the top of the tin to get the milk out. Abena discovered very quickly how, like many other things, the milk could go bad if not covered or preserved properly. Nana's soup was the absolute best, and Abena adopted the practice of licking her fingers, just like other children, to express her love for the delicious soup. The first time she attended a wedding party, she was fascinated by the colourful attire and mouthwatering food. The aunties were expected to bring a variety of dishes and delicacies, and the children took pleasure in identifying the tastiest ones. Eventually, they became experts in distinguishing the desirable food from the ones to avoid.

Life in Ghana consisted of more than just school
and household chores. She had the opportunity
to make friends and engage in playful activities,
which became the highlight of her holidays
and weekends (aside from attending church).
Abena then met Grace, who lived in the nearby

compound but went to a different school. Grace
taught Abena how to play *Tumatu*, also known as
hopscotch. She also introduced Abena to other
kids, and they had a lot of fun playing another
game called *Pilolo*, which combined hide and
seek with treasure hunting. These enjoyable

moments served as a great motivation for Abena to complete her homework and fulfil her domestic responsibilities. This was her routine for three years until her mother arranged for her to return to the United Kingdom, where she would rejoin her 'newly improved' family. She

had mixed feelings over this news. Even though this would disrupt her established routine, which she had grown accustomed to and would miss, she also longed for the presence of her parents.

What About Me?

Every day is the same, always boring and lame
Go to school and come back
Chores make their attack
There's no day I rest
Maybe, Sundays the best
Cause whether school or at home
I feel like I am not known
I have to do their bidding
No questions about what I want
Like they forbid me from sitting
What about me?

What About Me? (Continued)

Why not question how I feel?
Like I deserve to be free
My pain is also real
Let my voice be known
I am on my own
Listen to me
To what I have to say
Let me express myself my way

(A poem by Olivia Obafese, 11 years)

Chapter Three

NEW FAMILY

Transitioning from the sunny and vibrant city of Kumasi to the gloomy grey weather of London intensified the uneasiness that Abena felt ever since she found out she would be returning to live with her mother. Now that she was thirteen, she could look back on the past three years and truly appreciate the important role her grandparents had played in her life, especially Nanabarima's no-nonsense approach to discipline. Even before the plane touched down, Abena found herself already missing them, her friends, school, and the mouthwatering homemade African dishes.

Now, she was starting a new chapter in her life, with a different family from the one she had left three years ago. Her mother had found love again and had a baby boy. Abena felt a mix of excitement and caution as she eagerly anticipated meeting her stepfather and brother. She really hoped her mother had finally found happiness and that her new husband would provide the love and support her father couldn't. Although she missed her grandparents, she was ready to embrace this change with optimism. She straightened her backbone! She would be a loving and devoted daughter to her mother and stepfather. Hopefully, they would return the same.

Regrettably, this was not to be. Abena quickly learned that even though her mum had remarried and now had a career, she hadn't changed much emotionally. They still did not have that mother-daughter bond. True, she was provided for, and she attended a good school, but that was it. Over the next few years, two sisters were added to the family; for Abena, this was the best part of being with her mother. She doted on her siblings, and they looked up to her. Over the years, they were there for each other, which could not be said for her parents.

Abena had hoped that her stepfather would step into the role of a loving father, but her expectations were shattered. He was constantly belittling her with comments that made her feel worthless. He would always find a way to harshly criticise her cooking, her grades, and her appearance. The most painful part was that her mother never defended her or offered any support. As Abena grew older, nothing changed. One day, she had planned to attend an event and wore a beautiful dress her friends had always admired. As she appeared from the room, happy that she looked really good, she could hear her stepfather say harshly: "Abena! What are you wearing? Are you now a street girl? Not good at all. Not good! I don't know why you bother. You simply do not have the looks". Stung by his words, Abena abandoned her plans for the party and retreated to her room. Her youngest sibling, Afua, came running, and offered her a comforting embrace, "Don't listen to him, Sis. You are beautiful. Everything's going to be alright, you'll see. Stop crying". Although Abena managed to smile and reassure her little sister that she would be fine, she felt deeply hurt. Desperate for support, Abena tried to confide in her mother about the abuse she endured from her stepfather. "Mamme" she started, "Daddy is so nasty to me ...". As usual, her mother cut her off, dismissing her concerns and blaming her for provoking her stepfather. "And so what? If you had dressed well, he wouldn't have needed

to talk to you that way." Abena tried to explain further but her mum was not having it, "Look, you can see I am tired from work! Why are you trying to stress me? Are you the only one? My friends' daughters never give their parents any trouble". She tried again, "But..." "But nothing! You are the one with problems! Are you aware that Kisi, Miriam's daughter, is on track to qualify for a scholarship?" Abena fell silent. Her mum was right. She had fallen behind in her grades and she couldn't seem to turn it around. She was such a failure. Her mum's voice brought her back to the present. "Oh, by the way. Don't forget Aunty Dhakira's event on Saturday. Make sure you're ready on time and wear the attire I made for you and the girls. No slacking." With that, she stalked off to her room.

Abena had tried to communicate her distress to her mother, but she knew it was futile. She knew that her mother would not listen or empathise with her. In addition to this, Abena had to endure attending the family gathering, fully aware of the predictable outcome. This was not her first time dealing with extended family members and their issues.

"You look fantastic", Ekuwa, her cousin, exclaimed as Abena entered the room where the family event was taking place. She had decided to go ahead with her sister, Asante, to keep her mother quiet and to have as little contact with the aunties and uncles as possible. As she entered, she nosedived to the 'cousin area' to achieve this purpose. Her cousin, Ekuwa, was a bit of a rebel but also looked up to her which was refreshing. Abena raised her eyebrow at her compliment. "I know you are trying to make me feel good, but I'll take it", she smiled. "But you do!" Ekuwa replied. "Abena, stop taking the nasty comments over the compliments! It's not healthy. As for me, I don't care what people think or say; I will choose to live and love as I please". We both headed for the drinks stand, and she continued by asking, "Do you remember when Uncle Timmy said I was fat? After that, I went on one rubbish diet that wasn't working, and then I almost had depression!" She paused pensively as if remembering that painful period. Then

she spoke with the insight of someone older, "But I woke up one day and decided that I wasn't going to live up to his or anybody's expectations anymore!"

"Ekuwa!" Aunty Dhakira called out, rooting them out of their hiding place. "Why are you monopolising Abena and Asante? My dear, let

them come and say hello to Aunty Esi and others who are eager to see them too." Abena didn't have much of a choice but to quickly say hello and take her leave. But Aunty Esi wasn't having any of it. She insisted that Abena stay seated, and she was bombarded with questions about her time in Ghana, school, and future goals. "Abena, I'm not enjoying this conversation! I need more than those short answers you are giving! What are your plans after your exams? I hope you're not planning to sit at home. Going to university is important for our family, and the more graduates we have, the better." Aunty Esi took a generous swallow of her *Fufu* and *groundnut soup* before continuing. "Make sure you get good grades so that you're well-prepared for a worthwhile career." She looked at her enquiringly expecting a response. "Yes, Auntie. I'm doing my best," Abena responded, hoping that would be the end of it. "Come back here," her Auntie yelled as she made to leave. "I'm not finished! You need to choose a profession that will make us proud, one that is both lucrative and respectable. We already have a medical doctor in the family, but Law is just as good. What do you think?" Before Abena could say anything, her Auntie carried on. "You young people these days don't want to study and make good use of your time in school. You all want an easy life. Maybe you want to be... what do they call those people on the internet all the time? Social Media people. Hmmmm. And don't even think of being a musician. I know they make money, but it is still not meaningful work! The income is temporary". She appeared to be thinking some more, "I hear...". Auntie's sentence was cut off by the voice of Ekuwa, who with a short 'Excuse me' dragged Abena away with some made-up reason. "Thanks, Ekuwa" Abena sighed, "You are a lifesaver!"

On her way back home, Abena pondered over

the evening and asked herself, what chance do I have when my family's expectations of me are so high? No one cares about my aspirations. No one seems to be interested in how I feel. I can't even talk to anyone about my situation at home or how it is affecting me at school. How can I make them listen to me? Can anyone hear me if I think my thoughts loud enough?

Abena's stepfather continued to treat her in the most dreadful manner possible, and it wasn't until years later that she started to feel the full impact of the abuse she endured. She found herself unable to assert herself even over her young siblings. But she was not the only one facing difficulties in the home. Adwoa was having a hard time living with a man whose insecurities affected their relationship. She was tempted to leave on numerous occasions but felt compelled to stay because of the children and the shame of having another failed marriage. Leaving would only confirm her failure as a wife, and she didn't want to give people a reason to gossip.

It all came to a head when, during a bitter argument, Tom hit Adwoa. This was not an isolated incident, and she had never retaliated. But she and the children had had enough. Asante and her brother came to their mother's aid and called the police. He was so bitter that he turned on the children. "Is that how much you children respect me? Calling the police on your father? I am your father!" he ranted. After being detained by the police for one night, Tom moved out of the house. Adwoa didn't want to press charges but knew she could no longer live with him.

Abena was away when all this happened, and even though she was relieved that the abuse had come to an end, she knew that the family would continue to be traumatised in days and months to come.

A Child's Voice

Listen to the voice of a child
You will hear the truth of their words
Like a story to be heard
Learn from our honesty
That we deserve to be heard
For many years our voices have been hiding
But today it comes out

(Precious Airemuen, 10 years)

Chapter Four

SCHOOL AND FRIENDS

The drastic transition from school in Ghana to UK secondary education affected Abena profoundly. In this particular school, she was expected to think independently and be self-reliant, and the teachers did very little to support her dreams and aspirations. The lack of drive for success was strange to Abena. She missed the structure of learning in Ghana, the strict but guided input and mentorship of her teachers, and the community spirit that made learning fun.

Schooling in Ghana placed much emphasis on values, traditions, and cultural practices, and social studies was a major component of the curriculum. This helped plant the seed for Abena's passion for writing and storytelling. The folktale of Anansi the Spider, a popular trickster character in Ashanti Folklore in Ghana, further inspired her.

Still, despite her disenchantment with her school in the UK, it served as an escape from

the difficulties she faced at home. With a mother who lacked emotional support and an abusive stepfather, her mental well-being was declining. Unfortunately, the presence of bullies in school made it even more challenging for Abena, as they used every opportunity to pick on her when she tried to participate in class discussions actively. Being a non-native British student made her an easy target for taunts, and she would often be called names like 'goody two shoes,' 'suck-up,'

and 'bootlicker.' Surprisingly, the teachers did nothing to address this behaviour of her classmates or acknowledge Abena's dedication to learning. They only acted when she herself made mistakes. For instance, there was a time when her homework went missing, and she did not realise it until it was time to turn it in. Even though she suspected it was stolen by one of her classmates, she still got a harsh reprimand from Mr Maslow in front of the entire class. Abena felt as though everything was going wrong for her.

Thankfully, during this time, Abena found an ally in Tolu, who had recently migrated from her home country of Nigeria. Due to her different cultural background, Tolu stood out among the other students. Her oversized pleated skirt, unfashionable baggy blazer, and clunky school shoes attracted attention. Her schoolmates and teachers found the way she spoke, in broken English (pidgin), very amusing, and they usually burst out laughing when she was asked to read aloud in class. Abena suspected that they called on her just to get a laugh. When Tolu brought pounded yam and egusi for lunch, the other students sitting nearby wrinkled their noses at the strong smell, pointing and laughing, "Eewh". What's that? It stinks!". Despite facing similar

mistreatment from the students as Abena, Tolu remained unfazed and unapologetic about who she was. Abena admired Tolu's self-confidence, and her admiration grew even more when a bully snatched Abena's bag and scattered its contents on the floor. Tolu immediately stood up to the young man and shouted, "Is something wrong with your head? Leave her alone!" He backed off, and she then asked Abena, "Are you alright, my sister?" as she helped her gather the scattered items. Abena responded with a grateful smile, saying, "I'm fine, thank you so much." Little did they know that this incident marked the beginning of a lasting friendship.

Their friendship soon expanded to include several other students with similar characteristics from their shared emotional and family struggles. They formed a strong bond and decided to support each other in overcoming school challenges and achieving

success. Unfortunately, this outcome was not to be realised by all of them.

Yaw was a part of this group. At the tender age of 12, he was abandoned by his parents and subsequently taken in by social services. After a long and challenging process, he was eventually placed under the care of an uncle who showed little concern for his well-being. Yaw frequently skipped school and accumulated numerous detentions. His uncle was repeatedly summoned and apparently frustrated with caring for a pre-teen. He took advantage of every opportunity to remind Yaw that he was an ungrateful child destined for failure. Yaw's indifference to the reprimands angered his uncle more, and he punished him at every opportunity. He got slaps and kicks and sometimes had no food to eat. What his uncle and other people failed to see was the real reason for Yaw's academic difficulties, and he could not even articulate his struggles. After several times being unable to do his reading in class, Yaw would find reasons to disappear. He poured his energy into football, and his friends noticed that this was the only time Yaw was excited. Later on, it was confirmed that he had dyslexia, although it remained undiagnosed during that period of his life. He completed school with poor grades, giving his uncle another reason to criticise him. His situation worsened when he discovered that his uncle had neglected to assist him in resolving his immigration paperwork, which could have been easily accomplished while he was still a minor.

Upon reaching the age of 16, he was unable to further his education. He had to set aside his aspiration of becoming a footballer so that he could earn enough to hire a lawyer to address his immigration issues. Despite continuing to reside with his uncle during this time, no love was lost between them. Thankfully, he still had his friends and held on to hope that someday he would realise his dream.

Unlike Yaw, who could mix easily with people, Joshua was a timid and isolated young boy when he joined the school. He always seemed to lack sufficient food, and his school clothes were always dirty. With no idea of his father's whereabouts and a constantly ill mother who refused assistance for fear of judgment, Joshua was left to fend for himself. He loved his mother and resolved to do whatever it took to take care of her. Abena and the rest of the group provided as much support as possible. They would gather at the youth centre in the neighbourhood where Joshua lived at least once a week. The youth centre offered various activities to engage young people, but Joshua was mainly interested in the snacks provided. He would stay for as long as possible, assist with cleaning up, and then, with permission from the youth worker, take the leftovers home for his mother. Joshua's responsibility for his mother forced him to mature quickly, leaving him with no real childhood experiences to cherish. He appreciated having the supportive youth worker and his friends at the centre, but he still needed to keep his guard up.

Joshua's relationship with Abena and others began to change when he started socialising with a group of youngsters close to the youth centre. Abena grew suspicious when she saw Joshua's new sneakers and his flaunting of cash. Concerned, she approached him and asked about his sudden change in circumstances. Joshua assured Abena that everything was fine and there was no need to worry. However, they later discovered that Joshua had become a target of a well-known local gang that had manipulated him into engaging in illegal activities. Joshua felt trapped and frightened as he had unwittingly become a part of their criminal "family". Consequently, he became distant from his friends, not by choice but due to the circumstances he found himself in. His pressing needs closed his eyes to the true nature of the gang, and when he eventually realised their intentions, it was already too late.

He was ultimately expelled from school after being apprehended by the police for carrying a knife. Abena and Tolu were overwhelmed with sadness and self-reproach for not taking more action. However, considering the limited resources available to them and the shortcomings of both the educational system and their families, there was not much they could have done.

My Voice

In school and home,
My voice takes a flight
Lessons learned; stories shared
Families and school, a foundation prepared
At home, family embrace
Support and love, a safe place
Acceptance and understanding
Freely given
Empowering young ones to awaken
Through word and action, they confess
Their thoughts and dreams they express
School and family, a powerful blend
Shaping my voice from beginning to end

(Prisca Airemuen, 13 years)

Chapter Five

RELATIONSHIPS AND COMMUNITY

"Ahah, Abena! Is this the best you can do? 'D's and 'E's after all your mum has invested in you?!" This was the reaction of an 'Uncle' upon seeing her GCSE results. Seriously! What did he know about the 'investments' of her mother? If only he knew that these poor scores were a return on her mother's investments. But honestly, Abena wasn't surprised at all about the indignant reactions. In fact, she had been expecting them. The difference was that this time, at the age of 16, she wasn't going to stick around and endure their abuse and bullying. She had a plan; she would soon move in with Tolu, and once she had enough money, she would get an apartment of her own. She shared this plan with her siblings, who pleaded with her not to leave. Afua was devastated. "Sister Benaaa, why are you abandoning us? Who will we turn to when Mum starts stressing us?" she asked in a distressed voice. "Don't worry," Abena replied, "I won't be far away, and you can call me or pop in anytime."

Everything had gone as planned, and Abena had been living with Tolu for two years, during which time she took a short course and began working as a healthcare assistant. Soon after, she got her own place and became independent. Whenever she received her salary, she would spend it on clothing, jewellery, and cosmetics.

She became obsessed with always looking good and told herself that even when she started dating, she would ensure that her lifestyle was maintained. This was the uneventful life she was leading when she crossed paths with Kwesi.

Kwesi was tall, dark, and attractive and immediately caught Abena's attention. They began dating but soon realised that their vastly different backgrounds turned out to be a strain on the relationship. Abena loved to think of herself as cultured and mature, while Kwesi held firmly to some archaic African traditions, such as taking the 'man is the head of a woman' belief overboard. Despite living in the United Kingdom for many years, he acted in ways Abena had never been exposed to. For instance, she would excitedly tell him about a new movie and suggest seeing it at the cinema. Kwesi would reluctantly agree, turn up twenty minutes late and end up falling asleep halfway through the film. His

excuse? "I was tired. I'm not a fan of cinemas or movies anyway", he would say with no remorse. Still, despite his shortcomings, she wanted a man by her side. They dated for a few more months, and Abena decided that their differences were nothing to gloss over. She had projected her own desires onto him, only to realise that it was all a fantasy (just like her many expectations in life). She realised that many of her expectations seemed to be a figment of the imagination. She ended up unhappy with her job, and the money she received at the end of each month seemed to vanish quickly. She had no savings, no prospects, and felt very dissatisfied. She tried to shake this feeling for some time but couldn't.

Abena never lost touch with her family, mainly her sisters. She called up Asante. "You've been scarce, Asante. I came over the other day, and Mama told me you were out". "I know, Sis", Afua responded. "We keep missing each other. I was in church and got back really late". "That must have been a long service because I waited like forever". "Yes. The session was longer than normal but quite refreshing. How are you?" she asked. They gisted for some time, but not once did Abena talk about her unhappy situation. She did think to herself, though, that it was time to reconnect with the Church; maybe it would bring order to the chaos that was her life. "I feel so empty, and I need help," She said aloud. Soon after, she identified and started attending a church in the area, which helped a little. She also contemplated returning to school and becoming a better role model for her siblings. That was until she found out that she was pregnant.

After recovering from the shock, she pondered over her choices. Informing Kwesi was not really a problem; after all, he had never been opposed to having children. He took full responsibility, and even though he was willing to support pregnant Abena, he did not want a committed relationship with her. Tolu, her friend, was outraged. "Are you serious, Bena? From where I'm sitting, this guy wants to have the best of two worlds. He does not want to commit but still comes around to sleep with you whenever he wants to. Come on, Abena, he is taking advantage of you, and you know it. He knows you are in a vulnerable position and is using it to his benefit." "I know," Abena responded, "but I think that he will eventually commit since a baby is involved. And me I am willing to overlook our differences. I don't want to do this alone." Tolu rolled her eyes at her friend. "Abena, are we still here? You need to start having faith in yourself! Do not settle for a loveless relationship just because of the baby." She sighed, "You mentioned that this was your mother's experience, right? Don't let history repeat itself with you." When Abena didn't respond, Tolu said, "Okay, I know it's not up to me, so I concede. Kwesi can be involved in the baby's life, but you, my friend, need to be certain of what you want and trust in God to work it out for you."

Abena experienced a difficult first three months of the pregnancy. Her morning sickness was severe, and she was not motivated to go to work. She had already lost interest in it anyway, so she decided to stop going altogether. As a result, she found herself without a job and an eviction notice from her apartment by the time she reached her fifth month. She sighed. She couldn't postpone the evil day any longer. It was time for her to inform her mother about her situation, and she prayed that it would go as well as possible. Abena prepared herself for the expected 'fire and brimstone' and intentionally chose to go to the house on a Sunday after church, hoping that the fact that it was 'the day of the Lord' would soften the reaction from her mother. However, she was taken aback when she got no reaction at all. Adwoa was completely indifferent, and Abena was confused. It was almost as if she expected to one day get this news. Abena almost preferred her mother's anger to the coldness in her eyes. But at least she let her move back in, for which she was grateful.

The subsequent weeks and months were traumatic for Abena – physically, emotionally and mentally. Her mother refused to provide any support and she had to depend on her community, who stepped in to help regarding food, clothing and counsel. Adwoa would leave for work in the morning and return in the evening, never once inquiring about Abena's well-being. By the time the baby arrived, she was so depressed and overwhelmed that she feared that she would be deemed incapable of caring for her baby, leading to social services taking the child.

Despite Adwoa's disappointing behaviour, the community, friends and family gathered for the traditional naming ceremony eight days after the baby's birth. Kwesi and his family members attended and proudly named their baby girl Queen Ekua. Abena was grateful for the support of her community before, during and after the ceremony. They assisted with tasks such as washing, feeding, and cleaning, which evoked memories of being back home in Ghana. This support was instrumental in her recovery from the depression she experienced after childbirth.

After her recovery journey, which lasted almost a year, Abena was ready to resume her usual activities. She enrolled to pursue a degree in Health & Social Care, excelled in her exams and had various job opportunities on the radar. It was around this period that Abena started gaining the respect of her family members. Her Aunt Dhakira even reached out to her to get her to talk with her son, Danso. "He is constantly getting into trouble, always arriving late to school, and getting him away from his gaming console is a huge task. I don't know what else to do; maybe I should send him back home where life's difficulties will teach him a lesson," she concluded. "Oh dear, Auntie, it's not that serious yet. I will try to talk to him," Abena responded.

Abena had a strong desire to be a positive influence on her younger siblings and cousins, but she understood that it required both wisdom and patience. Additionally, she still had her own issues to deal with. She called on Danso to address his mum's concerns but made no progress. However, everything changed when she came across a flyer for a workshop aimed at children of Danso's age. The workshop focused on creating a game that combined football and mental health. After much persuasion, Danso felt motivated to take part in the learning process. After this breakthrough, Abena felt a strong sense of fulfilment.

Abena's appreciation for her extended family and the surrounding community increased during her recovery period. She would not have found the inner strength to persevere without their support. Reflecting on her past experiences, she realised that the expectations placed upon her by her family and community contributed to the pressure and feelings of depression she had previously faced. Nevertheless, as she navigated the challenges of motherhood and building a life for herself, she confidently believed that this dynamic had made her stronger and a positive role model for her younger siblings. The trauma she experienced during her early years intensified her feelings of low self-esteem, but it also reinforced her deep-rooted need for family connections.

Abena discovered that culture could be both

enjoyable and frustrating. The Ghanaian culture around her during recovery was always buzzing with activities, ensuring there was never a dull moment. While this could sometimes be helpful, it also meant there was no opportunity for much-needed silence at other times. Additionally, cultural differences can often create differences in perspectives. For example,

during a family meeting, a matter was brought up of an unruly son who refused to run an errand because he had plans with his friends. Such behaviour was unheard of in Ghana, but in the UK, it was different. Well, whether in Ghana or the UK, these 'plans with friends' were overruled by the intervention of the 'elders'.

Listening and Hearing

Listening comes in two ways
You can listen and not hear
But when you hear us
You can share our pain and share our joy
Listening to us and hearing us gives the
assurance that we are not alone
Therefore, hearing us makes us feel
safe and secure

(Jeannette Joycelyn Fosu, 10 years old)

Chapter Six

CAN YOU HEAR ME?

Abena's childhood experiences were a blend of trauma and enlightenment. At twenty-three, she couldn't shake the belief that these encounters — from enduring an abusive household to being uprooted from both the United Kingdom and Africa at different points, as well as becoming a young mother — all played a part in her feelings of sadness and insecurity. Particularly impactful was her witnessing the abuse inflicted upon her mother by the men in her life. Despite all of this, she was determined to be a better mother to her daughter, Queen Ekua. Although she still struggled with feelings of low self-worth, Abena was committed to unlearning the negative influences she encountered in the past and replacing them with positive values.

To Abena, the most valuable lesson she learned from her experience was that forgiveness is a vital aspect of relationships. Her relationship with her mother had been a constant struggle, and when her mother expressed a desire to talk to her one day after church, Abena immediately became guarded. "What have I done wrong this time?" she wondered.

Despite being an adult capable of making her own decisions, Abena still felt cautious around her mother and tried her best to avoid potential conflicts. When she arrived home and saw her mother sitting on the balcony, gazing across the field, Abena greeted her with a simple "Good evening, Mum. Hope you had a good day?" Her mother replied lukewarmly, "It was okay." Then, she turned towards her daughter, said, "Abena..." and suddenly burst into tears. Abena rushed to her side, filled with concern. This was shocking, as Abena had never seen her mother cry. The display of raw emotion deeply unsettled her.

"Abena, I want to apologise for all the pain I caused you. I was going through a difficult time and couldn't handle it. I directed my anger and resentment towards you, which was completely unfair". Adwoa said everything quickly, as if to get it all off her chest. "I am truly sorry". Abena was taken aback by her mother's sudden display of emotion and felt a mix of self-consciousness and embarrassment. However, Adwoa insisted on letting it all out. She told Abena that she truly loved her and that seeing her get pregnant brought back painful memories of her past. "I didn't want you to go through the same struggles I had, and I felt like a failure for not being able to protect you from hardship. I wanted to hug and love you, but it was so hard for me. Living here for so many years and seeing what you have gone through made me realise that I need therapy, especially if I want to have a better relationship with you and your siblings. I am still healing, so I want to appeal to you to be patient with me. But first, I need your forgiveness".

Abena had not recovered from her shock, and she pondered her options carefully, contemplating whether to express her thoughts or say what her mother wanted to hear. Eventually, she decided to speak up. Inhaling deeply, she uttered, "Mum, I hear you, and I forgive you". However, I feel compelled to share my heart with you. When I sought your help, I was in immense pain. As a child and later as a mother, I yearned for you to truly hear me. I pleaded for your attention and guidance but received silence instead. I longed for your affection, but

it was withheld. I couldn't understand why you had so much anger towards me." Gazing into her mother's eyes, she whispered, "If only you had truly listened." Upon hearing her daughter's heartfelt words, Adwoa wept uncontrollably, as if a floodgate had been unleashed. "I am so sorry, Abena; please forgive me. Please, my daughter".

"It's alright, Mum." She embraced her mother and ended up comforting her. "I understand the challenges you have faced with the men in your life. I also realise that you didn't want me to repeat the same mistakes you made. But there's a valuable lesson here, and it's not too late to make things right. My sisters and your granddaughter need you to support them. Our younger ones need to be listened to. We must remind ourselves that the old notion of 'Speak only when spoken to' or 'Lower your gaze when speaking to an adult' no longer applies to our generation. If we don't let go of these outdated cultural beliefs and listen to our children's doubts and fears, they will react negatively, including acting in rebellion. We don't always have to agree with each other, but let's strive to understand each other's emotions and work through them together. Then, we can fully experience the love we know you have for us. Please listen to us, Mother!"

Can You Hear Me?

Can you hear me?
My voice is powerful.
Well, not really!
Some people do it naturally.
Have their voice carry over the noise
and the talk
However, I always find myself asking
Can you hear me?
You don't seem to be listening.
I'm talking about something important here.
And you can't seem to tear your eyes
away from the phone
But it's fine. I'll wait,
I'll wait for my voice to be powerful
For it to carry over the noise and the talk
But even then, I find myself asking

Can you hear me?
I was telling the group a fun story
But now you have interrupted
And they are not listening to me anymore
They are listening to you
But it's fine, I'll wait.
I'll wait for my voice to be powerful, for it to
carry over the noise and the talk.
Actually, no
I'm done waiting
I deserve to be heard
Because my voice is powerful
And I'm done with asking
Can you hear me?

(Georgina Newborn, 14 years)

EPILOGUE

Back to the Present Day

Abena cuddled up to Femi on the sofa, preparing to watch their favourite drama series. "What's up, babe? You've been oddly quiet. I hope I haven't done anything wrong," he joked. She looked at him and smiled. "Don't worry, you're fine. It's just that I can't help but think about Esi, Queen's friend." She then proceeded to share what her daughter had told her about Esi's difficulties at home and how they brought back memories of her own past. Femi continued to listen to his wife; he could relate to everything she said; after all, he had had a front-row seat to all of her 'issues' earlier in their marriage. "We have really come a long way, Bena. Thank goodness for therapy." She gazed at him affectionately and said, "No, thank goodness for you – for being there all these years and loving Queen Ekua as your own. I couldn't have made it without you." Femi embraced her and said, "Now, tell me how you truly feel."

Abena thoughtfully responded, "I feel fortunate, and I am happy that Queen Ekua isn't going to go through what I went through. I also feel sorry about what Esi is currently experiencing. I want to use every given opportunity to help and nurture my daughter, Esi, and the younger generation around me. I want to use my experience positively."

That's what gave birth to *Wote Me Nka*, a

nonprofit organisation aimed at helping children and young adults who need support systems as they navigate through life. It proved to be her most rewarding decision, and her greatest satisfaction was seeing the positive transformation in the lives of those her organisation has helped.

Wote Me Nka? has become a household name in Abena's community and beyond. It means *Can You Hear Me?* in her native Twi language.

Can You Hear Me?

A Parent's Perspective

Yes, I can. In a way, you want me to.
You don't need to show me an attitude
before I can.
Don't raise your voice at me, but look into my
eyes for me to hear you.
I can hear you more than you think.
Knowing that I have been at your age before,
I know how it feels, even when
you need a hug and you don't get any.

Help me to understand you more because
I also go through bad days.
Meeting your needs as a parent is my priority.
So you have to help me to give you all the care
and support you need in life
in order for you to reach your full potential.
I can hear you as long as we can work together.

(Stella Twene, A Parent)

GLOSSARY OF TERMS

Term	Meaning
Akwaaba	This is the official welcoming expression used in Ghana. It means "welcome" in the Twi Ghanaian language.
Nana	Title of a Monarch or 'Your Highness' in Ghana.
Nanabarima	An expression used in Ghana for male grandparent.
Kumasi	Known as the Garden City in Ghana
Kenkey	Staple swallow food in Ghana
Pilolo	An outdoor game among Ghanian children, also translated to "time to search for".

Term	Meaning
Tumatu	A game among Ghanian similar to Hopscotch
Twi	A variety of the Akan languages spoken in southern and central Ghana
Fufu	A West African swallow meal commonly made by pounding cassava and unripe plantain and accompanied by soup.
Egusi	A creamy, nutty soup made from melon.
Groundnut soup	A popular soup dish in West Africa made from groundnuts.
Pounded Yam	A classic Nigerian dish made by pounding boiled yam into a smooth and dough-like consistency.
Wote Me Nka?	Can you hear me? in Twi language.